LAUGH YOUR SQUAREPANTS OFF!

SIMON AND SCHUSTER
First published in Great Britain in
2012 by Simon & Schuster UK Ltd
1st Floor, 222 Gray's Inn Road,
London WC1X 8HB
A CBS Company

All titles included previously published
as individual titles by Simon & Schuster
UK Ltd and Simon Spotlight, an imprint
of Simon & Schuster Children's Division,
New York.

A CIP catalogue record for this book
is available from the British Library

ISBN 978-0-85707-232-0

Printed in Great Britain

10 9 8 7 6 5 4 3 2

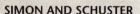

Based on the TV series *SpongeBob SquarePants* created by
Stephen Hillenburg as seen on Nickelodeon

nickelodeon

SpongeBob SquarePants

LAUGH YOUR SQUAREPANTS OFF!

SIMON AND SCHUSTER/NICKELODEON

Chuckle and Cringe

SpongeBob's Book of Embarrassing Stories

by David Lewman

SIMON AND SCHUSTER/NICKELODEON

SpongeBob NoPants!

by SpongeBob

Life in Bikini Bottom is great! But sometimes it can be a little embarrassing. Like the time I ended up in Mrs Puff's classroom dressed in nothing but my underwear.

I was getting dressed one morning, and I couldn't decide which belt to wear with my square pants — the black one? Or the other black one?

Just then, Patrick stuck his head through my window. "Hi, SpongeBob!" he called.

"Hi, Patrick!" I answered. "How did you climb up to my window?"

Patrick looked puzzled. "This is *your* window?"

Then he asked if I wanted to go jellyfishing, but I told him I had to go to boating school. And now I was late!

I ran all the way to school, sliding into my chair just in time. The other students were all pointing and laughing. What was so funny? I looked down, and saw that I didn't have on any pants! I'd forgotten to put on my belt, so my pants fell off on the way to school!

Boy, was my face red. And yellow, of course.

Blockhead!

by Patrick

Oh, yeah, I've been *real* embarrassed.

One time I was helping SpongeBob build a new fireplace out of wood. (It ended up not working very well for some reason.) First I helped carry the nails. Then I helped pick up all the nails that had fallen onto the floor, which was all of them. I helped carry boards, too. But when SpongeBob started nailing the boards together, I asked if I could try. He said, "Sure, buddy, but be careful!"

Somehow the very first board I worked on got stuck to my forehead. Which was really embarrassing, because you're not supposed to wear a hat indoors.

The end.

Pirate Day!

by Squidward

I'm embarrassed
just about every single day
when I go to work at the
Krusty Krab. But one day
Mr Krabs managed to make my
miserable job even more
humiliating than usual.

"It's Pirate Day at the
Krusty Krab!" Mr Krabs
announced, grinning.

"What does that mean?"
I asked.

"It means you wear this
costume," he answered,
thrusting a pile of heavy
clothes into my hands. "And
don't forget to say 'Ahrrr!'"

I went into the restroom and put on the clothes Mr Krabs was forcing me to wear. Then I looked in the mirror. I looked ridiculous! Well, I thought, maybe no one will come to the Krusty Krab today.

But when I walked out of the restroom, there was a huge crowd chanting, "Pirate Day! Pirate Day! Pirate Day!" I guess I should have expected that.

Everyone in Bikini Bottom saw me in that ridiculous, itchy outfit. At the end of that long day, I said, "This shouldn't be called Pirate Day. It should be called Embarrass Squidward Day."

"No, Squidward," said SpongeBob, pointing to a calendar. "That's next Thursday!"

In a Pickle!

by Sandy

I don't get embarrassed easy. Shoot, I'm from the great state of Texas! What have I got to be embarrassed about?

But there was one time I had a little . . . accident. As I was leavin' my treedome to go to SpongeBob's house, I grabbed my air helmet. But before I could put it on, it slipped out of my fingers and . . . *crash!*

Now what was I supposed to do? I couldn't just go out in all that water without my helmet!

I ran back into the kitchen, and on the top shelf was a big jar of pickles. If I emptied it, could it work as a temporary air helmet?

I didn't have time to get out my step ladder, so I jumped up, grabbed at the jar — and it fell right on my head!

As the pickles floated past my eyes, I thought, Well, at least no one's here to see this.

But then I heard SpongeBob walk in. "I couldn't wait for you to come over, Sandy, so I decided to come to your house!"

Even the green pickle water couldn't hide my blushin'.

Lucky Penny

by Mr Krabs

I remember the most embarrassin'
thing I ever did. It was when I was
just a little baby.

I was crawlin' around, exploring the world. With me claws, I could pick up anythin' that looked interestin' and put it in me blue diaper.

I found a shiny shell and put it in me diaper. A beautiful little grain of sand — into me diaper. A broken bit of coral — into the diaper she goes!

Then, as I was crawlin' along, I spotted somethin' different. It was round, and a little dull, and brown. Should I put it in me diaper? I thought. Nah! It's not shiny and pretty. I crawled on past.

But behind me I heard a bigger boy exclaim, "Oh, boy! A penny!"

It was a penny, and I didn't pick it up! Oh, the terrible shame of it! The only lucky thing was that I was already bright red, so you couldn't see me embarrassment.

Believe me, I never made that mistake again!

Size Matters

by Plankton

Say what you like about me, I don't get embarrassed easily. Furious, yes. Maniacal, certainly. Evil, of course. But not embarrassed.

There is one thing that does embarrass me a little, though. No, not my size! WHAT'S WRONG WITH MY SIZE?! YOU WANT TO MAKE SOMETHING OF IT?!

Sorry. Anyway, there is one tiny embarrassing secret I keep. And it seems to come out at the worst possible times.

Last year, I was attending the annual villains' conference at the convention centre in downtown Bikini Bottom. Everybody was there – the Dirty Bubble, Man Ray . . . you name it.

Just as I was about to get up and give my speech, "Keeping Your Evil Plans Fresh," some joker dropped in carrying a big sign with my first name on it and a finger pointing to me. sheldon, it read. Everyone started to laugh. AT ME!

There's nothing wrong with the name Sheldon. But as a name for a villain . . . well, it doesn't exactly strike terror into the hearts of my victims. I'd just as soon keep it quiet.

I was steaming. Luckily no one could see since I am very, very small.

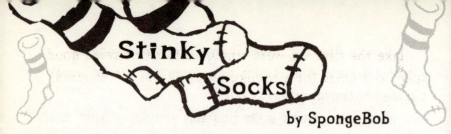

Stinky Socks

by SpongeBob

Patrick's my best friend, but sometimes his ideas put us right on the express train to Embarrassment City.

Like the time we were trying to think of some good scary costumes for a spooky party. "I know!" shouted Patrick. "We'll be Sockheads!"

"What are Sockheads?" I asked.

"Guys with socks on their heads!" answered Patrick.

"What's scary about that?" I asked.

"Have you ever smelled dirty socks?" Patrick retorted. He grabbed two big, smelly socks and yanked them over our heads.

At the party, people weren't scared of us. In fact, I was pretty sure I could hear them giggling every time we walked by.

But that wasn't the most embarrassing part.

With the sock over my eyes, I couldn't see. Suddenly I felt cold and wet, and I heard a loud crash! I had walked straight into the punch bowl!

We did win a prize, though — for smelliest costume.

Shall We Dance?

by Patrick

SpongeBob's my best friend, but sometimes he has ideas that turn out much different than we expect.

Like the time he thought it would be a nice surprise for Squidward's birthday if we learned to dance the Foxtrot. Whatever that is. I guess it's something Squidward likes.

So we took a ballroom dance class, and we were ready.

We both wore top hats and carried canes to perform at Squidward's party. But we hadn't practiced with the canes. At the end, when we threw our arms in the air, both of our canes went flying! SpongeBob's cane hit Mr Krabs in the claw, and mine popped three balloons.

Squidward was embarrassed, but SpongeBob and I thought it was pretty funny!

Music to My Ears

by Squidward

SpongeBob has embarrassed me more times than I can count. Like when he and Patrick tried to do some kind of dance for my birthday - puh-leeze!

Or the day I remembered at the last second that it was the annual Bring-a-Guest meeting for Clarinet Club. I was running around begging people to come along — the mail carrier, a policeman, some crazy old lady who was walking by — when SpongeBob overheard me and said he'd love to come along.

I knew it was a terrible idea, but I was desperate. The rules of Clarinet Club are very strict.

We hadn't been at the meeting for more than a minute when SpongeBob started saying I was the best clarinet player in town, and that he knew it was true because I had told him so!

This made the other club members a little peeved.

"Show 'em, Squidward!" SpongeBob exclaimed gleefully. "Play something right now!"

To shut him up, I started to play, but I was so nervous that I made mistake after mistake. I was embarrassed, my teacher was embarrassed — even my clarinet was embarrassed!

But not SpongeBob. "You know, Squidward," he said proudly. "I think that's the best I have ever heard you play!"

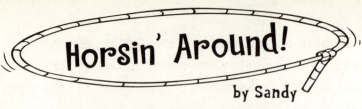

Horsin' Around!

by Sandy

Hey, I just remembered another time I got a little bit embarrassed. It was at the Bikini Bottom Rodeo.

I'd been doing great in every event — sea cow herdin', Alaskan bull worm ridin', and giant clam wrestlin'. So I was really looking forward to the ropin' contest.

My lasso was ready to go. I started twirlin' it around, fixin' to toss it over the head of a wild seahorse.

But just as I was startin' to toss my rope, SpongeBob called, "Hi, Sandy!" from the viewin' stands. Without thinkin', I answered, "Hi, SpongeBob!" and waved my hand.

Unfortunately it was my lasso tossin' hand. Instead of goin' around the neck of the seahorse, my lasso went right around the judge of the ropin' contest!

Well, I didn't win that part of the rodeo. And instead of callin' me Sandy Cheeks, you could have called me Red Cheeks!

Money Matters

by Mr Krabs

I guess it was a wee bit embarrassin' the time I ended up in the Krusty Krab in me pyjamas.

For weeks I'd had trouble sleepin'. I spent all night, every night, worryin' that somethin' bad was happenin' to me money.

Finally, one night after frettin' for hours, I counted me money into the dawn. By the time I was done countin', the sun was high in the sky. I was so exhausted that I fell deeply asleep. And I had the most peculiar dream.

I dreamed that I was going for a walk through a beautiful kelp forest where money grew right on the plants. Money had fallen onto the ground all around me, and all I had to do was pick it up!

Suddenly I heard a familiar voice sayin' me name: "Mr Krabs? Are you all right?" It was SpongeBob!

I woke up and found myself standin' in the Krusty Krab. I'd been sleepwalkin'! Me claws were full of sand I'd picked up, thinking it was money! But even worse: I was standing right in the middle of the dining area, wearin' nothin' but me nightshirt!

I can still hear all the customers laughin'. Still, the humiliation was worth it — what a wonderful dream!

The Rumour Mill

by SpongeBob

One afternoon at work I overheard two customers saying that they'd heard the Krusty Krab was going out of business!

I ran into Mr Krabs's office. "Mr Krabs!" I screamed. "Please don't close the Krusty Krab! Please, please, please, please, please!"

Mr Krabs calmed me down and told me he had no intention of closing his restaurant. "That story, me boy, is just a rumour," he said.

"What's a rumour?" I said. He explained that a rumour was a story spread around as if it were true. "Why do people do that?" I asked. Mr Krabs said he guessed people thought it was fun.

The next day Patrick and I were sitting around with nothing to do. Patrick said he wanted to do something fun. I remembered what Mr Krabs had told me, so I suggested we start some rumours.

Patrick and I ran all over Bikini Bottom. "Squidward's head is made of cheese!" we cried.

"Sandy is really a fish in disguise!"

"Mrs Puff is married to Plankton!"

We told rumours to anyone who would listen – and that was a lot of people!

But it didn't take very long for everybody to trace the rumours back to me and Patrick, and they were real mad at us. Boy, was I embarrassed. I'll never start another rumour again.

Unless maybe it's about myself! Did you know I'm secretly Mermaidman?

The Mad Scientist

by Plankton

I admit it. One time in high school I was kind of embarrassed.

In chemistry class, we had to figure out what went into this secret formula. I didn't feel like doing it, so I tried to steal the formula from my lab partner, Eugene Krabs. But I got caught, which was embarrassing.

The teacher gave me a failing grade. I vowed I would DESTROY HIM! But I never got around to it.

Come to think of it, admitting this is pretty embarrassing too. Let's just forget the whole thing. Or would you like me to DESTROY YOUR BRAIN?! That's what I thought.

Date Night

by Mrs Puff

I like Eugene Krabs – I really do. At the end of a long day of trying to teach SpongeBob how to drive, it's nice to have a quiet, relaxing dinner with Eugene.

But sometimes he can be a little embarrassing.

Last Tuesday, for example, we were in a very nice restaurant, enjoying our desserts. Suddenly one of the other diners dropped a penny. Everyone could hear it rolling across the floor.

Eugene's eyes bugged out. His claws started to click open and closed, faster and faster. Then he dove onto the floor to get the penny!

Everyone stared at him as he grabbed the penny and shouted, "Ah, penny! You've made me the happiest crab in the sea!" Then he started kissing the penny over and over.

And he didn't even leave a tip.

THUMBSUCKERS

by SpongeBob

Once when Patrick and I were out on a walk, he said, "I'm hungry, SpongeBob."

"Sorry," I said. "I don't have any snacks." Then I remembered something. "Hey! Remember when we were little and we'd suck our thumbs? It tasted great!"

"Yeah!" said Patrick, sticking his thumb in his mouth. I sucked my thumb too.

We were walking along, happily sucking our thumbs, when Squidward rode by on his bike. He yelled, "Hey, babies! Want your bottles?"

"Yeah, Squidward! That'd be great!" answered Patrick, smiling and giving a drool-covered thumbs-up.

I was pretty embarrassed. Especially since Squidward called me SpongeBob ThumbSucker for a month.

A Cry for *HELP!*
by Larry the Lobster

As a totally muscular lifeguard, I don't have a lot to be embarrassed about.

But one morning when I was out jogging, I heard someone cry, "Help! Help! I'm going under!"

I realized the distress call was coming from the Krusty Krab, so I burst through the front doors. "Don't worry! Larry the Lobster is here!" I announced. "Who's going under?"

Patrick stuck his head out from underneath a table. "Uh, I am!" he said. "I dropped the toy from my Krusty Meal."

"Then why did you yell 'Help, help'?" I asked.

"It looked kind of dark under there," said Patrick.

I was embarrassed. But *Patrick* should have been embarrassed.

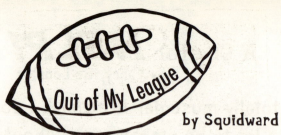

Out of My League

by Squidward

One time in high school I was completely embarrassed in front of a girl I liked.

I was talking to her in the hallway, when my rival, Squilliam Fancyson, came up and started bragging about how he was captain of the chess team.

Before I knew what I was doing, I blurted out, "Oh, yeah? I'm trying out for the football team!"

Squilliam's eyes lit up. "Great!" he said sarcastically. "We'll be there to watch your every move!"

Tryouts were after school that day. And I knew nothing about football! During lunch, I ran into the library and read everything I could about the game.

On the field that afternoon, the coach asked me what position I was trying out for. The only position

I could remember from the book was the quarterback, so that's what I said.

He shrugged and handed me three balls. "Fine," he said. "Let's see a few passes, Tentacles."

I looked nervously up into the stands. Sure enough, there were Squilliam and the girl I liked. Squilliam cupped his hands around his mouth. "Show us what you got, Squidward!" he yelled.

I picked up the first ball and threw it. It landed about three feet behind me. Squilliam laughed.

I picked up the second ball and tossed it. It hit the coach on the back of his head.

Before he could stop me, I picked up the third football and hurled it as hard as I could. It sailed across the field . . . and right through a gymnasium window! Meanwhile I fell over backward into a big puddle of mud.

Squilliam was laughing so hard he could barely breathe. It was very embarrassing.

But the girl felt so sorry for me that she went out with me for a month!

Ticket to Ride
by Mermaidman

As a superhero it's my job to fight EVIL! But sometimes fighting crime can get a little embarrassing.

Like the time I heard the Sinister Slug was jaywalking in downtown Bikini Bottom. I ran out of the Mermalair and leaped into the Invisible Boatmobile. Or what I thought was the Invisible Boatmobile, since I landed on the ground with a thud.

I caught a bus downtown and spotted the Sinister Slug. Sure enough, he was crossing the street in the middle of the block!

As I ran toward the fiendish criminal, I tripped over one of my slippers and fell flat on my face. He was getting away!

I dashed across the street, but I forgot to go to the crosswalk, so a policeman gave me a ticket for jaywalking. Needless to say, the Sinister Slug escaped.

ADULT SWiM
by Barnacleboy

Embarrassing stories? I got a million of 'em! But I'm too old to remember 'em.

Except maybe this one. A couple of years ago I decided it had been a long time since I'd gone swimming. I used to do a pretty mean dog paddle. So I headed down to *Goo Lagoon*.

I arrived just in time for adult swim, which was great. My dog paddle kicks up quite a splash, so I need plenty of room.

But the second I put one toe in the water, I heard the lifeguard's whistle. "What's the problem?" I asked the big, muscular lobster.

"This is adult swim," he answered.

"So?" I snapped back.

"So you're Barnacleboy. During adult swim, no *boys* are allowed in the water!" he barked.

I slunk back to my beach towel and waited until adult swim was over. I may be sixty-eight years old, but I can still blush.

♡ Puppy Love ♡

by SpongeBob (and Gary)

My pet snail, Gary, is the greatest pet in history! I take good care of him, so most of the time he's happy. But one time I think he was kind of embarrassed.

I was walking him when he spotted someone walking a beautiful girl snail. Gary tugged on his leash, trying to get over to her. But when Gary reached her, I could tell the beauty of this mollusk made him nervous.

He stood there for a moment, trembling.

Then he coughed up a huge shellball! The girl snail looked disgusted and slid away.

Before that day, I didn't know snails could blush.

All Wrapped Up

by Patrick

One time I was getting ready for a costume party.

I was trying to use this bandage, but I got all tangled up in it.

It was so embarrassing. It completely ruined my mummy costume. The end.

Three Cheers For Pearl!

by Pearl

Last week at school I had a majorly embarrassing day.

I was at cheerleader tryouts, feeling a little nervous. But the coach told me to relax. Because I was on the squad last year, I was pretty sure to make it again this year.

Just then Daddy burst into the gym. "Go, Pearl!" he shouted. "The best little cheerleader in all the Seven Seas!" I thought that was totally humiliating, until he turned to the door and waved his claw. "Okay, come on in!"

"What's going on?" I asked desperately.

Daddy said, "They can't turn down a cheerleader who's got . . . HER OWN CHEERLEADER!"

Suddenly SpongeBob ran in wearing the most ridiculous cheerleading outfit I'd ever seen — baggy tights, a fuzzy headband, and a sweatshirt with my picture on it!

"*P-E-A-R-L* SPELLS 'PEARL'!" SpongeBob screamed. Then he tried to do a cartwheel but slipped on the shiny gym floor and slid right into the bleachers with a crash!

Everyone was pointing and laughing, so to distract them, I did the tryout cheer. The coach congratulated me, and said anyone who could remember a routine through all that chaos definitely belonged on the squad. Whew!

Spin Class
by Sandy

Y'all gotta be real careful when you're exercisin'. Otherwise you just might embarrass yourself.

The other day I was trainin' in my exercise wheel. I decided to really push myself to the limit, so I just kept runnin' faster and faster and faster . . . until the wheel came loose! It started rollin', and took me right out of my treedome, across town, and smack dab into the side of SpongeBob's house!

Not only was I embarrassed, but I got a lot of pineapple juice in my eye. That stuff stings!

Scared Silly

by the Flying Dutchman

It seems like every time I decide to haunt Bikini Bottom, something embarrassing happens!

The last time I sailed me ghostly ship over that little town, I spotted SpongeBob SquarePants out on a walk with his pet snail.

This is a perfect opportunity to scare the daylights out of that little yellow fellow! I thought.

I quickly parked me ship, hopped out, and breathed a mighty blast of fire at the invertebrate. *Har, har!*

Chuckling to myself, I returned to me ship. But I saw there was a ticket on the steering wheel — I'd parked in a loading zone!

Embarrassing? You'd better believe it! Or I'll HAUNT YOU FOR THE REST OF YOUR DAYS! AH HA, HA, HA, HA, HA!

Only kidding. I got better things to do. Like earn some money to pay for this ticket.

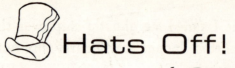 # Hats Off!

by Patrick

This one time, I was walking through a dark room. Then suddenly I bumped into someone.

"Excuse me," I said. No one said anything back.

"I said, 'Excuse me,'" I repeated. Still nothing. How rude!

So I started a big fight. Grabbing, shaking, growling — the whole bit.

Turns out I was fighting a hat rack.

And I lost.

Burst Your Bubble

by the Dirty Bubble

You know, people think supervillains never get embarrassed, but it's not true. We do.

Once I was right in the middle of a big fight with Mermaidman and Barnacleboy, and I was sure I was going to win.

But just as I was about to deliver the final blow, something really embarrassing happened.

I popped.

By the time I got myself reinflated, they'd thrown me in jail. And everyone could see my dirty blushes.

Candid Camera
by SpongeBob

This is a really embarrassing picture of me from a party.

I can't remember how my pants fell down or why I'm wearing my protective karate headgear.

All I know is, I hope no one has a copy of this picture, especially hidden in some secret box.

Wait a minute! Now *you* have a copy! Oh, no!

I'M WITH THE DUMMY!

by Patrick

I bought this really great shirt. It was so funny!

But then when I wore it, I was really embarrassed.

Why, you ask? I will tell you, gentle reader.

Because I realized that everyone I was hanging out with was a dummy!

Well, I guess that's enough stories for now. As you can see, embarrassing things happen to everyone, so it's okay to feel embarrassed now and then.

After all, no one's perfect *all* the time!

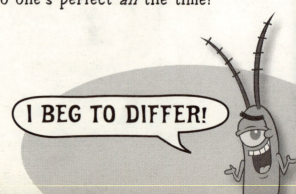

I BEG TO DIFFER!

Nautical Nonsense

A SpongeBob Joke Book

BY WENDY WAX

SIMON AND SCHUSTER/NICKELODEON

Why were SpongeBob's suspenders sent to jail?
For holding up his SquarePants.

What goes "Ha, ha, ha, plop!"?
SpongeBob laughing his head off.

What happened when SpongeBob sat on the chewing gum?
He became SpongeBob ChairPants.

Who is the snootiest sponge in Bikini Bottom?
SpongeSnob.

Why does SpongeBob prefer saltwater?
Because pepperwater makes him sneeze.

Where does SpongeBob point his sneeze?
Atchoo!

What did SpongeBob say to the Flying Dutchman?
How do you boo?

Who didn't clean his pineapple?
SpongeSlob.

SpongeBob: What doesn't get any wetter no matter how hard it rains?
Patrick: The ocean.

Why did Patrick bring a chocolate bar to his dentist appointment?
He wanted a chocolate filling.

Why does Patrick prefer to swim at night?
He's a starfish.

Why did the bubble gum cross the road?
Because it was stuck to SpongeBob's shoe.

**What was wrong
with Patrick's
pencil story?**
It didn't have a point.

**Why did Patrick walk as
he played the guitar?**
He wanted to get away
from the noise.

What is the Flying Dutchman's favourite kind of party?
A come-as-you-were party.

Why did Squidward play his clarinet while standing on a chair?
So he could reach the high notes.

Why did Squidward keep his clarinet in the fridge? So he could make cool music.

How does Squidward spell "disaster"?

S -P -O -N -G -E -B -O -B.

Squidward: Ouch! I threw out my back again.
SpongeBob: Check the trash before it's picked up!

Customer: Waiter! This coffee tastes like sand!

SpongeBob: That's because it was only ground this morning.

Knock-knock.

Who's there?

Dewey.

Dewey who?

Dewey have to eat
Krabby Patties again?

What happened when the Flying
Dutchman lost his anchor?
He haunted for it.

Why do some people call Mr Krabs a "doughnut"?
Because he loves money.

What is Mr Krabs's favourite part of the football game?
The quarterback.

How does Mr Krabs double his money?
By folding it in half.

How much does Mr Krabs eat?
Just a pinch.

What are two things Mr Krabs refuses to serve for lunch?

Breakfast and dinner.

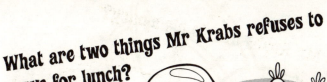

What happened when the Flying Dutchman got a job at the Krusty Krab?

He became the Frying Dutchman.

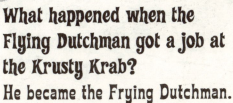

Why did Plankton stick a hose in Mr Krabs's ear?
He was trying to brainwash him.

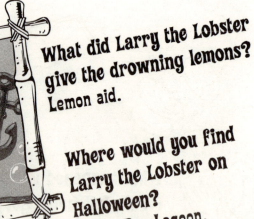

What did Larry the Lobster give the drowning lemons?
Lemon aid.

Where would you find Larry the Lobster on Halloween?
At the Boo Lagoon.

What does SpongeBob call Gary when he's riding in the passenger seat?
His carpet.

How did SpongeBob stop Gary from leaving slime in the backyard?
He put him in the front yard.

What did Pearl become on her trip to the Arctic?
A blue whale.

What musical did Mr Krabs plan to take Pearl to see on her birthday?
Fiddler on the Reef.

NOW SHOWING...
Fiddler on the **Reef**

What did they do when the musical was sold out?
They saw a dive-in movie instead.

What did SpongeBob call Patrick
when he fell in the swamp?
Muddy buddy.

If Gary got in trouble, where would he go?
Snail jail.

How does Gary keep in touch with his family? Snail mail.

Mrs Puff: SpongeBob, have your eyes ever been checked?
SpongeBob: No, they've always been blue.

Sandy: What do you call milk that is too far away to see?
SpongeBob: Pasteurized.

Why did Mrs Puff wear sunglasses to school?
She had bright students.

Who did Mermaidman become when he got lost in the Arctic Ocean?
Brrr-maidman.

How much did Patchy the Pirate have to pay to get his ears pierced?
A buck an ear.

Who wears an eye patch and is always itchy?
Scratchy the Pirate.

How did SpongeBob make a jellyfishing net?
He sewed a bunch of holes together.

Patrick: What does a jellyfish have on its tummy?

SpongeBob: A jelly button.

SpongeBob: What is the best way to catch a jellyfish?

Patrick: Have someone throw it to you.

Patrick: What buzzes, wobbles, and flies?
SpongeBob:
A jellycopter.

SpongeBob: What do you call a polar bear in Bikini Bottom?
Patrick: Lost.

Sandy: How does a boat show affection?
Patrick: It hugs the shore.

SpongeBob: What did one fish say to the other?
Squidward: If you keep your mouth closed, you won't get caught.

Books for Sale!

A Tourist's Guide to Bikini Bottom
by N. Joy Yerstay

Surfing Down Sand Mountain
by Howell I. Ever-Dewitt

The Krusty Krab Diet
by Watson Thimenue

Getting Rid of Plankton
by X. Terman Aite

Caring for a Pet Snail
by Walket Wunsaday

Sandy the Speedy Squirrel
by Sherwood Lyke Tewkatcher

How to Stop Procrastinating
by Alex Playne Layder

SpongeBob's Secret to Life
by M. Brace Itt

Mrs Puff: What's the capitol of Bikini Bottom?
SpongeBob: The letter B.

SpongeBob: What do you call two pieces of seaweed that get married?
Sandy: Newlyweeds.

Mrs Puff: What gallops through Bikini Bottom?
Patrick: A seahorse.

Knock-knock.
Who's there?
Doug.
Doug who?
Doug a hole in the sand.

What would you get if you cloned SpongeBob five hundred times?
A SpongeMob!

Why didn't the judge believe the Flying Dutchman?
Because he could see right through him.

Who haunts underneath SpongeBob's bed?
The Flying Dustman.

What is easy for SpongeBob and Patrick to get into but hard for them to get out of? Trouble.

How did SpongeBob make a bandstand?
He took away their chairs.

How did SpongeBob get straight As in Mrs Puff's class?
He used a ruler.

What kind of steps did SpongeBob take when Squidward chased him out of the Krusty Krab?
Great big ones.

Why did Patrick install a knocker on his rock?
He wanted to win the No-Bell Prize.

When does the Flying Dutchman usually appear?

Just before someone screams.

Why was it windy at SpongeBob and Patrick's bubble-blowing show?
Because of all their fans.

Why did Patrick put a strawberry under his pillow?
He wanted to have sweet dreams.

Where in Bikini Bottom did Squidward see an annoyed cashier?

In the mirror.

Squidward: Where do fish go when they don't feel well?

SpongeBob: To a sturgeon.

SpongeBob: What do you call a fish with no eyes?
Patrick: A fsh.

Patrick: Do fish ever have holidays?
SpongeBob: No, they're always in schools.

SpongeBob: What smells like fries and is covered with lint?
Squidward: The Dusty Krab.

SpongeBob: What lives at the bottom of the sea and carries a lot of fish?
Mrs Puff: An octobus.

Where is Patchy the Pirate's treasure chest?
Under his treasure shirt.

Mr Krabs: Why did the fish tell excuses?
SpongeBob: To get off the hook.

What do you get when you cross Dracula with Patchy the Pirate?
A vampirate.

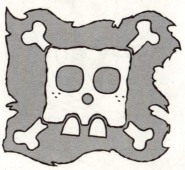

Why didn't SpongeBob do well on his report card?
Because his grades were below C-level.

How does SpongeBob know the sea is friendly?
It waves.

What game do Patrick and SpongeBob like to play?
Name That Tuna.

Mr Krabs: Why did the fries run out of the restaurant?
Patrick: They were fast food.

What did SpongeBob break by saying its name?
Silence.

Who is Squidward's favourite writer?
William Sharkspeare.

Why doesn't Plankton serve doughnuts?
He doesn't like the idea of the hole business.

Patrick: What lies at the bottom of the ocean and twitches?
Squidward: A nervous wreck.

Knock-knock.

Who's there?

Sir.

Sir who?

Sir-prise! The book is over!

SpongeBob's
BOOK OF
EXCUSES

by Holly Kowitt

SIMON AND SCHUSTER
/NICKELODEON

Table of Contents

Excuses, Excuses

Mr Krabs: Why did you bring your pet snail to work with you?

SpongeBob: He needs to come out of his shell.

Mrs Puff: Why don't you get As and Bs?

SpongeBob: I want to be a "sea" student!

Mr Krabs: Why did you miss work yesterday?

Squidward: I didn't miss it at all!

SpongeBob's Top Ten

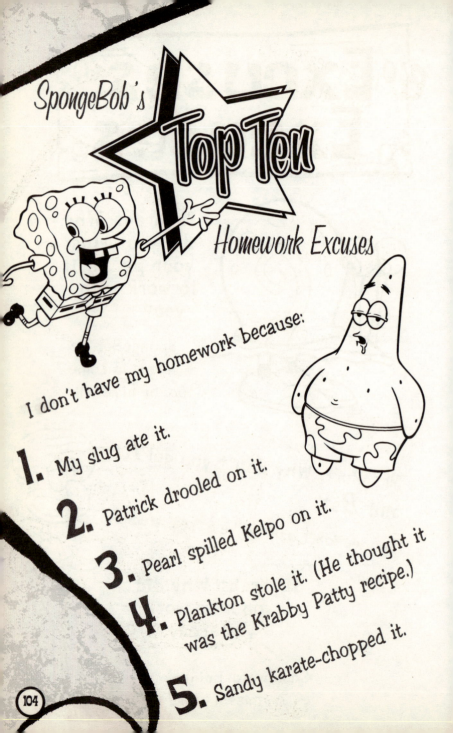

Homework Excuses

I don't have my homework because:

1. My slug ate it.

2. Patrick drooled on it.

3. Pearl spilled Kelpo on it.

4. Plankton stole it. (He thought it was the Krabby Patty recipe.)

5. Sandy karate-chopped it.

6. It was eaten by Nematodes.

7. It was swallowed by giant clams.

8. It was sucked into my reef blower.

9. Mermaidman zapped it with his laser button.

10. My bubble buddy borrowed it and never gave it back.

**SpongeBob:
There were two
cookies in the
jar last night, and
this morning
there's only one.
How do you
explain that?**

Patrick: It was so
dark, I guessed I
missed it!

Mrs Puff: Why did you go jellyfishing instead of writing your book report?

SpongeBob: Book report? I thought you said, "Brook report!"

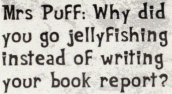

Mr Krabs: Why do you keep stealing the Krabby Patty recipe?

Plankton: I'd buy it from you, but I'm a little short.

SPONGEBOB'S Top Ten EXCUSES

FOR FLUNKING THE DRIVING EXAM AGAIN

1. I forgot to wear my lucky underwear.

2. I swerved to avoid a killer guppy.

3. I thought it was "Opposite Day," so I tried to do everything wrong.

4. I enjoy the test so much, I'm hoping to take it thirty-nine more times!

5. I didn't feel well - I had a haddock.

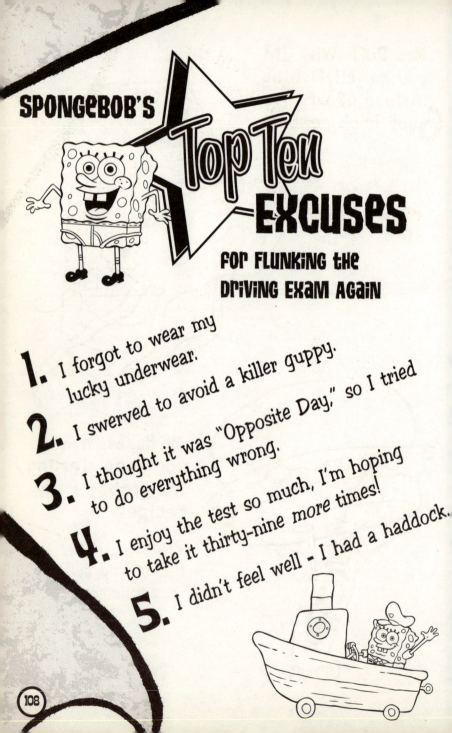

6. I stopped when I heard the seaweed yelling, "Kelp! Kelp!"

7. I could hardly hear Patrick on the walkie-talkie.

Can you help SpongeBob come up with three more excuses?

Write them here:

8. _____

9. _____

10. _____

Mrs Puff: Why are you always late for school?

SpongeBob: They're always ringing the bell before I get here!

Mr Krabs: Why do you always get in trouble?

SpongeBob: Once I get in, it's hard to get out.

Why didn't Mrs Puff believe the Flying Dutchman's excuse?

She could see right through it.

Mr Krabs: Why are you so behind in Krabby Patty orders?

SpongeBob: I don't know, but I'm trying to ketchup!

SpongeBob: Why can't you ever stand still?

Sandy: If I do, I'll go nuts.

Teacher: Why are you putting on lipstick in class?

Pearl: I thought it was a make-up exam!

Squidward: Why can't you leave me alone?

SpongeBob and Patrick: You're our favourite stick-in-the-sand.

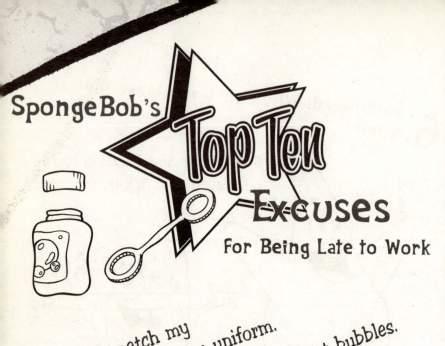

SpongeBob's Top Ten Excuses

For Being Late to Work

1. I had to match my athletic socks to my uniform.

2. I had to blow some very important bubbles.

3. I had to help Mermaidman catch Man Ray.

4. I had to recharge my shell phone.

5. I had to walk the snail.

6. I was waiting for the piano tuna.

7. My foghorn alarm clock broke.

8. I had to cheer up a blue whale.

9. I woke up on the wrong side of the pineapple.

10. I'm actually early for work — tomorrow!

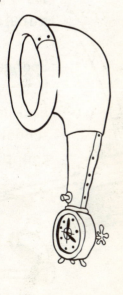

KARATE CUTS

Mr Krabs: Why are you doing karate at work?

SpongeBob: I thought I was supposed to punch the time clock!

Ms Puff: Why are you doing karate at school?

SpongeBob: It's my back-to-school chopping!

Squidward: Why are you doing karate in the kitchen?

SpongeBob: I wanted to show I could cut the mustard!

Excuuuuuuuuuuuuse Me!

Patrick: I'm afraid my son can't go to school today.

Mrs Puff: Oh, that's too bad. And to whom am I talking?

Patrick: This is my father.

Squidward: Why are you blowing bubbles?

SpongeBob: Because I already blew my nose.

Salty Answers to Stupid Questions

Customer: Do you sell Krabby Patties?
Squidward: No, we make them laugh. They're very picklish.

Squidward: Are you going jellyfishing?
SpongeBob and Patrick: No, we're catching some rays. Stingrays.

SpongeBob: Did you get into an accident?
Mrs Puff: No, I purposely crashed the
boat, so you would ask that question.

SpongeBob: Are you playing the clarinet?

Squidward: No, I'm
tickling it till it laughs.

Mr Krabs: Is that your pet snail?

SpongeBob: Shhhh! Mollusks are
people, too,
you know.

SpongeBob: Are you asleep?

Patrick: No, I'm using my body to hold
this rock down.

SPF 45

SALTY ANSWERS at the Krusty Krab

Customer: There's a Fly on my Krabby Patty!

Squidward: Don't worry, we won't charge you extra for it.

Customer: Are Krabby Patties healthy?

Squidward: I've never heard one complain.

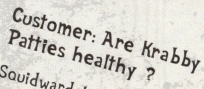

Customer: Will my Krabby Patty be long?

Squidward: No, it'll be round, sir.

Customer: This Krabby Patty tastes Funny.

Squidward: Then why aren't you laughing?

Customer: Do you have seaweed salad on the menu?

Squidward: No, I wiped it off!

Mr Krabs: How'd you find your Krabby Patty, mate?

Customer: Easy. I just moved the fries, and there it was!

125

Even More Excuses

Mr Krabs: Why did you spill sea onion ice cream on your new Krusty Krab uniform?

SpongeBob: My old one was in the laundry!

Pearl: Daddy, why aren't you paying attention?

Mr Krabs: Um . . . how much do I have to pay it?

Mrs Puff: Why are you raising your hand before I'm finished?

SpongeBob: I'm not! I'm hailing a crab.

Squidward: Can you dimwits keep down the noise? I can't even read!

Patrick: Too bad. I've been reading since I was a little starfish.

SpongeBob: Why don't you take the garbage out?

Patrick: We don't like the same movies!

NOTES FROM THE UNDERGROUND

Ahoy, teacher!
Please excuse my darlin'
Pearl from gym class.
She hurt her fin carrying
a bucket o'clams at the
Krusty Krab.

So she shouldn't
be asked to
do any kind
of exercise,
except cheerleading
practise. Or I'll sue
for ever'thing you've got.

Yours truly,
Mr Krabs

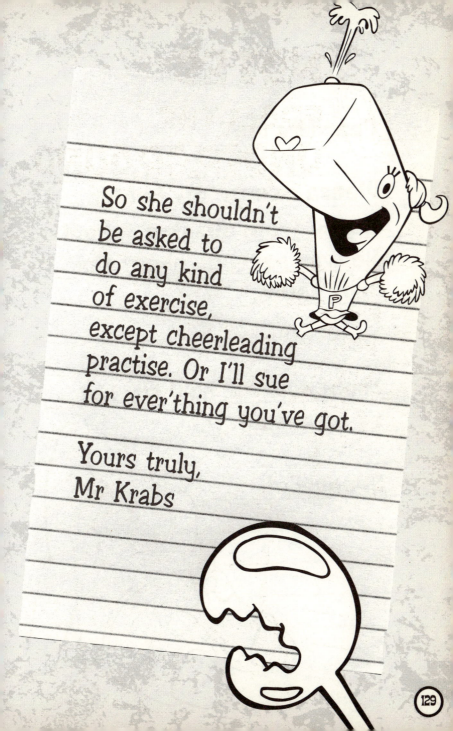

Dear Mrs Puff,

Please excuse my bubble buddy from missing school. He was nervous about the "pop" quiz.

From now on, he'll try not to be absent.

SpongeBob

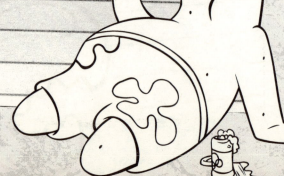

from the desk of **Mrs Puff**

SpongeBob,

I'll give your bubble buddy another chance, but frankly I don't know what you see in him...

Mrs Puff

Dear Mr Krabs,
Please excuse SpongeBob for missing work, but he has been struck down by the dreaded Suds, which cause sniffling, sneezing, and complaining.

He must stay in bed for three days, drink plenty of Diet Dr. Kelp, and watch *Mermaidman and Barnacleboy*. This is the only known cure.

Sincerely,
Dr. Fishman

Dear Mrs Puff,

My daughter couldn't take her boating exam because she was just too chicken.

Henrietta Hen

134

from the desk of **Mrs Puff**

Eggs-cuses, eggs-cuses!

–Mrs Puff

Patrick's mum: Patrick brought a note home from school.

Patrick's dad: What did it say?

Patrick's mum: They want a written excuse for his presence.

Patrick: The snail ate my homework.

Mrs Puff: But you don't have a snail!

Patrick: It was a stray!

Sandy: Why are you wearing fake muscles?

SpongeBob: The muscles are real – the rest of me is fake.

137

SPONGEBOB'S Top Ten EXCUSES

FOR LOSING THE KRUSTY KRAB TALENT SHOW

1. My hands were clammy.

2. Choosing socks that match is a talent!

3. Squidward's better since he switched to electric clarinet.

4. I didn't know Patrick could carry a tuna!

5. I shouldn't have agreed to do a ballet with Plankton.

6. My pineapple's too crowded for more trophies.

7. I can't compete with Patrick - he's a star!

8. I didn't know that was the judge's head.

Can you help SpongeBob come up with two more excuses?

Write them here:

9. ‒‒‒‒‒‒‒‒‒‒‒‒

10. ‒‒‒‒‒‒‒‒‒‒‒‒

Mix 'n' Match 'n' EXCUSE ME!

First match a character in Column A with a problem in Column B. Then on the next few pages write an excuse for that character!

Column A

SpongeBob

Squidward

Patrick

Mr Krabs

Pearl

Plankton

Mrs Puff

Sandy

Column B

waking up late

missing an appointment

losing a shoe

forgetting to make dinner

burning a Krabby Patty

spilling food on a Krusty Krab customer

not writing a thank-you note for a birthday gift

driving too fast

Excuses

1. _SpongeBob_ 's excuse for
(character)

Waking up late **is:** _So_
(problem)

the alwrm is broke.
(excuse)

2. _Squidward_ **'s excuse for**
(character)

missing an appointment **is:** _He_
(problem)

was up Late.
(excuse)

3. <u>patrick</u> 's excuse
(character)

for <u>lossing a</u>
<u>shoe</u> (problem)

is: <u>was</u>
(excuse)

<u>a burglar</u>.

4. <u>Mr Krabs</u> 's
(character)

excuse for <u>getting</u>

<u>to make dinner</u>
(problem)

is: <u>the oven isnt</u>
(excuse)

<u>working</u>.

5. <u>pearl</u> 's excuse for <u>burny</u>
(character) <u>a krabby Patty</u>

_____
(problem)

is: _____.
(excuse)

142

6. _____ 's excuse for
      (character)

_____ is: _____.
      (problem)   (excuse)

7. _____ 's excuse for
      (character)

_____ is: _____.
      (problem)   (excuse)

8. _____ 's excuse for
      (character)

_____
      (problem)

_____

is: _____
      (excuse)

_____

_____.

SPONGEBOB'S EXCUSE FOR WRITING THIS BOOK

No one else would write it for me!

THE END

Blizzard Bluster!

SpongeBob's Book of Frosty Funnies

by David Lewman

SIMON AND SCHUSTER/NICKELODEON

How did SpongeBob pick his favourite flake?

"Eeny, meeny, miny, snow . . ."

Mr Krabs: Why don't winter clouds make good roommates?

Patrick: They spend the whole night snowing.

Patrick: What game do snowflakes like best?

SpongeBob: Tic-tac-snow.

Squidward: What did the starter say in the race between two winter clouds?

Sandy: "Ready, set, snow!"

Squidward: Knock, knock.
SpongeBob: Who's there?
Squidward: Snow.
SpongeBob: Snow who?
Squidward: 'S no way I'm going out in that cold, wet stuff.

Did the huge snowstorm do much damage in Bikini Bottom?

No, everything turned out all white.

Mrs Puff: Who's great at painting and is always cold?

Squidward: Vincent van Snow.

How did Patrick feel when he saw the new snowfall?

It was love at first white.

Pearl: Why did the piece of ice break up with the piece of snow?

Plankton: He turned out to be a real flake.

SpongeBob: What do you get when you cross cereal with snow?

Patrick: Corn flakes.

FLAKES

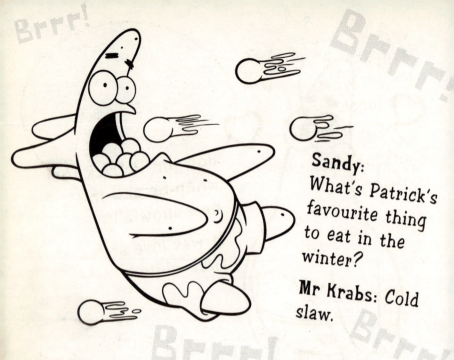

Sandy: What's Patrick's favourite thing to eat in the winter?

Mr Krabs: Cold slaw.

Pearl: What did the snowwoman do when the snowman asked her out?

Mrs Puff: She gave him the cold shoulder.

Mr Krabs: What do you get when you slice lunch meat during a snowstorm?

Plankton: Cold cuts.

Brrr! Brrr! Brrr!

Why didn't Patrick perform in the ice show?

He got cold feet.

Brrr!

Brrr!

Why couldn't Sandy follow the Alaskan Bull Worm through the snow?

The trail had gone cold.

Patrick: Knock, knock.
SpongeBob: Who's there?
Patrick: Scold.
SpongeBob: Scold who?
Patrick: 'S cold out here, isn't it?

Why did Plankton bring a hammer to the skating party?

He wanted to break the ice.

Why did Patrick try to lick the freezing pond?

He'd heard it was icing.

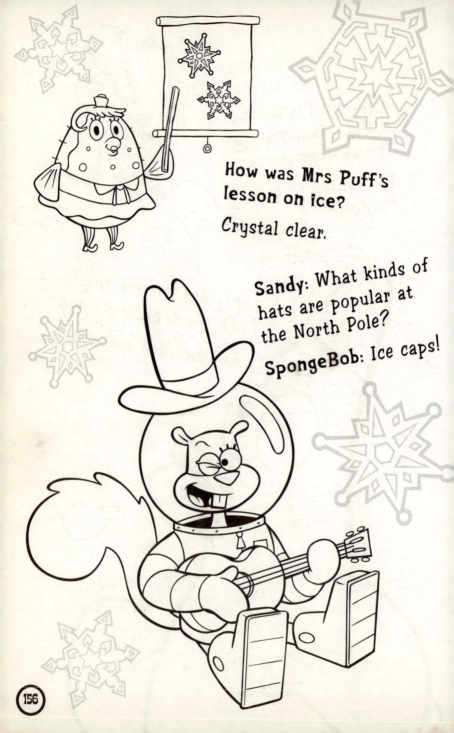

How was Mrs Puff's lesson on ice?

Crystal clear.

Sandy: What kinds of hats are popular at the North Pole?

SpongeBob: Ice caps!

Patrick: Why were the snowflakes all dressed up?

SpongeBob: They were going to a crystal ball.

What do young snowballs like to play at recess?

Freeze tag.

What happened when the Dirty Bubble tried to act in the ice show?

He froze up.

What do you get when you cross Sandy's tree with a pile of snow?

Driftwood.

Patrick: Do snowflakes make good students?

Mrs Puff: No, they keep drifting off.

Sandy: Was the snowfall a big hit in Bikini Bottom?

Mrs Puff: Yes, it took the town by storm.

What did Patrick sing as he ran into the snowstorm?

"We're off to see the blizzard!"

Why did Sandy jump on a jellyfish during the blizzard?

She wanted to ride out the storm.

Sandy: When are shoes like an icy sidewalk?

SpongeBob: When they're slip-ons!

How did Patrick do on his skating test?

He slipped by.

What happened when the cops chased Man Ray onto the ice?

He gave 'em the slip.

How did SpongeBob score a run during the snowstorm?

He slid home!

Why did Patrick walk to work with SpongeBob on the icy day?

He just went along for the slide.

What is SpongeBob's favourite snowy day game?

Slide-and-seek.

Why did Patrick cry loudly during the blizzard?

He wanted to make a snow bawl.

SpongeBob: What has a carrot nose and glides through the ocean?

Squidward: A snow-manta ray.

Pearl: What did the snowflake say to the sidewalk?

SpongeBob: "Let's stick together."

Mr Krabs: Why did the snowman keep getting bigger and bigger?

Patrick: He was on a roll.

SpongeBob: What happens when snowmen get mad?

Mr Krabs: They have a total meltdown.

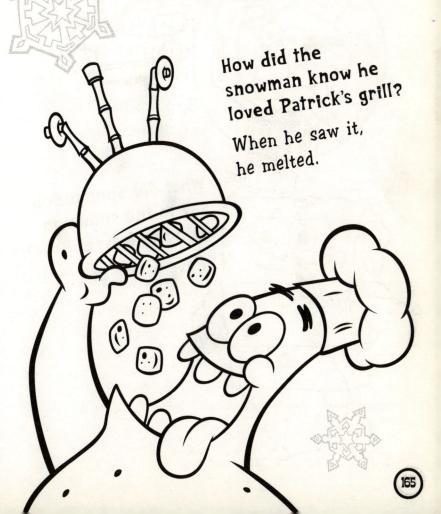

How did the snowman know he loved Patrick's grill?

When he saw it, he melted.

Barnacleboy: What do snowmen like to do on hot days?

Mermaidman: Chill out.

What did SpongeBob say to the snowman going to Mussel Beach?

"Have a nice drip!"

Brrr! Brrr! Brrr! Brrr! Brrr!

Patrick: Why don't snowmen ride bikes?

SpongeBob: They hate to puddle.

Patrick: Are snow sandwiches good?

SpongeBob: Yes, they melt in your mouth.

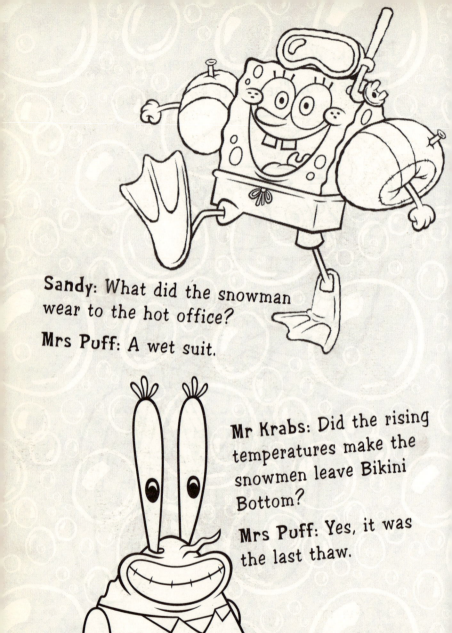

Sandy: What did the snowman wear to the hot office?

Mrs Puff: A wet suit.

Mr Krabs: Did the rising temperatures make the snowmen leave Bikini Bottom?

Mrs Puff: Yes, it was the last thaw.

Barnacleboy: Who wears a mask and steals ice and snow?

Mermaidman: A *brrr-glar*.

Sandy: What do you get when you cross a donkey and a glacier?

Squidward: A *brrr-o*.

What does Patrick
use to slide down
a snowy hill?

A SpongeBobsledge!

Why was Squidward
grouchy after he
tried tobogganing?

He got up on the
wrong side of
the sledge.

How did SpongeBob feel when he went off the ski ramp?

Jumpy!

What did Sandy do when SpongeBob suggested they try the ski ramp?

She jumped at the chance!

Mrs Puff: Which fish moves best on the ice?

Mr Krabs: The skate.

SpongeBob: Why did the parrot go to the skating rink?

Painty the Pirate: To play ice squawky.

How did Patrick score a goal in his very first hockey match?

Beginner's puck.

Why did Mr Krabs want to join the hockey team?

He heard he got to chase a buck.

Squidward: Which bird is best at hockey?

Sandy: The seagoal.

What's the coldest thing SpongeBob puts in a Krabby Patty?

Iceberg lettuce.

What did the snowman say when Plankton stole his nose?

"See if I carrot!"

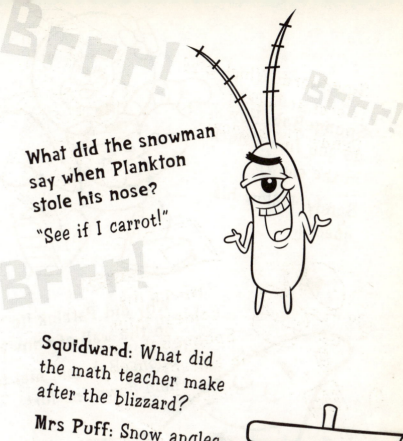

Squidward: What did the math teacher make after the blizzard?

Mrs Puff: Snow angles.

SpongeBob: How do you find a duck in the snow?

Sandy: Follow his quacks.

Why did Patrick lie on the wall of snow?

SpongeBob told him to hold down the fort.

Patrick: Is cocoa bad?

SpongeBob: Yes, it's always getting into hot water.

Mr Krabs: What do electric eels drink on snowy days?

Plankton: Hot *shock*olate.

SpongeBob: Was the cocoa mad at the marshmallows?

Patrick: No, he was just letting off steam.

Mr Krabs: Which dog keeps you warm in the winter?

Sandy: An Irish Sweater.

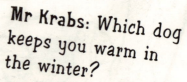

How did the snowman feel when SpongeBob covered him in coal?

He got a lump in his coat.

Patrick: What did the two fingers do on the cold day?

Pearl: They fell in glove.

Why did SpongeBob think he was fired on the snowy day?

Mr Krabs gave him the boots.

Mr Krabs: What do bakers wear on cold days?

SpongeBob: Ear muffins.

Sandy: What did the daddy truck say to the baby truck on the snowy day?

Squidward: "Why don't you go outside and plow?"

SpongeBob: Why do teeth talk so much on a cold day?

Patrick: They can't stop chattering.

Mrs Puff: What's the best grade to get on a freezing cold day?

Patrick: D-frost.

What happened to the Flying Dutchman when he sailed through the snowstorm?

He got a terrible case of frostboat.

Sandy: What do you use to catch frozen fish?

Mr Krabs: Frostbait.

What's the difference between having your fingers frozen and being scared of Mr Krabs?

One's a case of frostbite, and the other's a case of boss fright.

Sandy: When is a dog like a chilly day?

Plankton: When it's nippy.

Why did Plankton stay outside through an entire blizzard?

He wanted to be king of the chill.

Patrick: Which cold breeze is the smartest?

Squidward: A sharp wind.

Brrr!

Brrr!

Why did Patrick drag his bed out into the blizzard?

He'd heard there were sheets of ice and a blanket of snow.

Brrr!

185

Why did Mr Krabs go digging for money in the drift?

He'd heard it was a snow bank.

Why do the coldest customers get their Krabby Patties first?

Because it's first numb, first served.

Sandy: Which skating move do gorillas do best?

Squidward: The figure ape.

Painty the Pirate: Which pirate is the coldest?

The Flying Dutchman: Ahrr, that be Bluebeard!

What's Mr Krabs's favourite frozen treat?

Snow coins.

Why did Pearl stick her face in the fresh snow?

She wanted to powder her nose.

SpongeBob: What do you get when you cross an oyster with fresh snow?

Mr Krabs: Clam powder.

Patrick: Why did the little snowflake rise from the ground?

SpongeBob: His mum told him to flurry up.

Squidward: Which sea serpent moves best through a blizzard?

Plankton: A snowmob-eel.

SpongeBob: When is snow ready to travel in a ball?

Patrick: When it's all packed.

Mr Krabs: What do you call a hog pen made out of ice?

Sandy: A pigloo.

Patrick: What did the mama ice say to the little boy ice?

SpongeBob: "That's enough of your wisecracks!"

SNAP!

Chill out!

(We're done.)

FUNNY-SIDE UP

A Tasty Joke Book

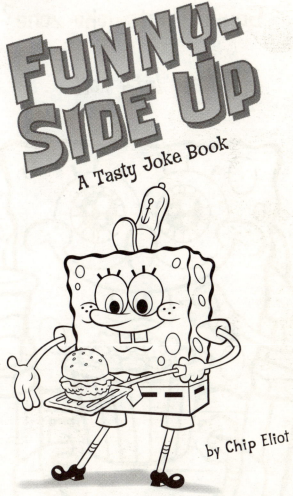

by Chip Eliot

SIMON AND SCHUSTER/NICKELODEON

Are you ready to navigate your way through the yummy SpongeBob SquarePants joke zone?

Okay, let's roll . . .

How does SpongeBob like his eggs?

Funny-side up.

Why did Patrick hold a stone and a Krabby Patty bun to his ears?

He wanted to hear some rock and roll.

JELLYFISH
JAM
BAND

SpongeBob: Patrick, will you join me in a cup of ice-cold lemonade?

Patrick: No, I don't think there's room for both of us.

Why did SpongeBob bring a tub of margarine to Mrs Puff?

He was trying to butter her up.

Why couldn't the egg lend Patrick any money?

Because it was broke.

What happened when SpongeBob ate one plate of spaghetti too many?

He went pasta point of no return.

Why did Mr Krabs want a job at the bread Factory?

Someone told him he'd make a lot of dough.

Mr Krabs: Once when i was shipwrecked, i lived on a small can of beans For a week.

SpongeBob: That's amazing! I'm surprised you didn't fall off.

Mr Krabs: Try some of my seaweed salad. It will put some colour in your cheeks.

Sandy: Who wants green cheeks?

Patrick: I'll have a Krabby Patty, Mr Krabs.

Mr Krabs: With pleasure.

Patrick: No, with tartar sauce.

What is Squidward's favourite fruit?

Sour grapes.

Squidward: Mr Krabs, how do you make a gold-medal Krabby Patty?

Mr Krabs: Easy. Just add fourteen carrots.

Patrick: Why is my Krabby Patty all squished?

SpongeBob: You told me you were in a hurry and that I should step on it.

Why does Squidward complain whenever he eats?

He likes to whine and dine.

Mrs Puff: I'd like a Krabby Patty, and make it lean.

SpongeBob: Which way?

Mrs Puff: Do you have lobster tails?

Mr Krabs: Yes, once upon a time there was a little lobster . . .

Mrs Puff: What fruit can you find everywhere in the ocean?

Pearl: That's easy. Currants.

Why did SpongeBob study all the old grease stains left on the grill at the Krusty Krab?

Mrs Puff said he should learn about ancient Greece.

Why did Patrick swallow a bunch of coins?

His mother said it was lunch money.

What did SpongeBob say when he saw the brand-new griddle at the Krusty Krab?

"Ah, the grill of my dreams!"

Pearl: What kind of cup can't you drink out of?
Patrick: A cupcake.

Why did Patrick toss a peach into the air?

He wanted to see a fruit fly.

Mrs Puff: What is this fly doing in my alphabet soup?

Mr Krabs: Learning to read?

KRINCH

KRINCH

KRINCH

Patrick: This Krabby Patty is way too rare. Didn't you hear me say well-done?

Squidward: Yes, I did. Thank you very much.

What do sailors like to eat for lunch in Bikini Bottom?

Submarine sandwiches.

SpongeBob: Patrick, why have you been staring at the carton of orange juice for three hours?

Patrick: It says, "Concentrate!"

How did Mr Krabs learn to cook?
He took ten greasy lessons.

Patrick: SpongeBob, can you fix dinner?

SpongeBob: I didn't even know it was broken.

Mr Krabs: How was your chicken soup?

Sandy: It was fowl.

Plankton: Do you take orders to go?

SpongeBob: Yes.

Plankton: Well then – GO!

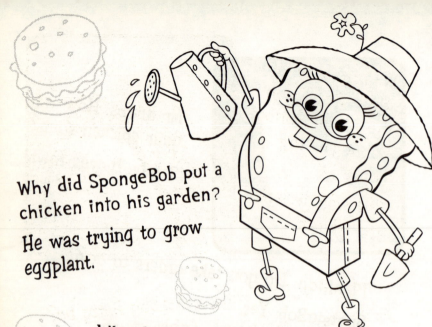

Why did SpongeBob put a chicken into his garden?

He was trying to grow eggplant.

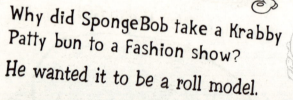

Why did SpongeBob take a Krabby Patty bun to a Fashion show?

He wanted it to be a roll model.

What happened when Pearl won the Bikini Bottom hot-dog-eating contest?

She was declared the wiener.

Sandy: How long will my Krabby Patty be?
Mr Krabs: It won't be long. It will be round.

Sandy: What kind of shoes can you make from bananas?

Patrick: I don't know.

Sandy: Slippers.

Who brings candy to all the good boys and girls in Bikini Bottom in the spring?

The Oyster Bunny.

Why did Sandy put sugar under her pillow?

She wanted to have sweet dreams.

Why did Patrick quit his job at the doughnut factory?

He was sick of the "hole" business.

Pearl: Why is it impossible to starve on a beach?

Sandy: Because of all the sand which is on it.

What does King Neptune like to drink?

Royal tea.

Why did Patrick put a Frankfurter in the Freezer?

He wanted a chilly dog.

What does a pirate have in common with corn that costs a dollar?

Both are a buck an ear.

SpongeBob: Did you hear about the egg that laughed itself silly?

Patrick: No, what happened?

SpongeBob: It cracked up!

SpongeBob: What do astronauts put on their sandwiches?

Sandy: Launch meat.

KRUNCH

Where can you see hamburgers dance?

At a meatball.

KRUNCH

KRUNCH

Patrick: What is your stew like today?

Mr Krabs: Just like last week's, only a week older.

KRUNCH

Why do clams and mussels not like to share?

Because they're shellfish.

Pearl: Did you hear the one about the banana that got sunburned?

Patrick: No.

Pearl: It began to peel. Did you hear the one about the lunchmeat?

Patrick: No.

Pearl: It's a bunch of baloney. Did you hear the one about the stale cookie?

Pearl: Yeah, it was really crummy.

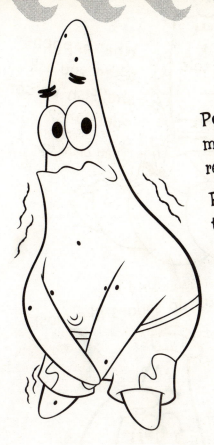

Pearl: What did the mayonnaise say to the refrigerator?

Patrick: Please close the door. I'm dressing.

What kind of lettuce did they serve on the *Titanic*?

Iceberg.

What happens when you ask shellfish personal questions?

They clam up.

What kind of fruit do sailors like most?

Naval oranges.

Mrs Puff: What fruit conquered the world?

SpongeBob: Alexander the Grape.

SpongeBob: What do you call fake spaghetti?

Squidward: Mock-aroni.

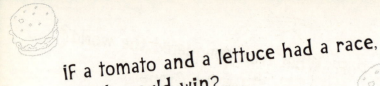

If a tomato and a lettuce had a race, which would win?

Lettuce, because it's always a head.

SpongeBob: What vitamin should you take to improve your vision?

Squidward: Vitamin See.

Why did Patrick take a dozen eggs to the gym?

He wanted them to get some eggs-ercise.

Why did Patrick throw sticks of margarine out the window?

He wanted to see butter fly.

What do you call SpongeBob when he sings and drinks soda at the same time?

A pop singer.

What's the smallest room in the world?

A mushroom.

What does SpongeBob's daily diet consist of?

Three square meals.

Why does Patrick like to talk to a cornfield?

Because it's all ears.

What sandwich is always scared?

A chicken sandwich.

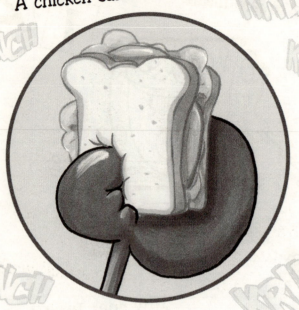

SpongeBob: What do you give a lemon when it needs help?

Sandy: Lemon-aid.

What did Patrick say to the pickle?
"You're dill-icious!"

Why did Patrick want a job in the salt and pepper Factory?

He was hoping to find seasonal work.

What do sea monsters eat?
Fish and ships.

SpongeBob: Why are tomatoes the slowest vegetable?
Mr Krabs: They're always trying to ketchup.

Mrs Puff: I asked you to write a composition on cheese yesterday. You didn't hand anything in. Why not?

SpongeBob: The tip of my pen kept getting clogged with cheese.

SpongeBob: Mr Krabs, do you know how to make a lobster roll?

Mr Krabs: Sure. Just take a lobster to the top of a hill and push!

Mr Krabs: SpongeBob, why is it taking you so long to fill the saltshakers?

SpongeBob: It's really hard getting the salt through the little holes on top.

Patrick: How much is a soda?

Mr Krabs: A dollar.

Patrick: How much is a refill?

Mr Krabs: It's free.

Patrick: Well then, I'll take the refill.

Sandy: SpongeBob, tell me the joke about the butter.

SpongeBob: No, you'd only spread it around.

Sandy: Then tell me the one about the egg.

SpongeBob: Oh, that one will crack you up.

Sandy: Did I tell you the one about the banana peel?

SpongeBob: No.

Sandy: It must have slipped my mind.

SpongeBob: You should go wash your face. I can tell what you had for breakfast today.

Patrick: Oh, yeah? What did I have for breakfast today?

SpongeBob: Oatmeal.

Patrick: Sorry, you're wrong. That was yesterday.

SNAP!

SpongeBob: Grandma, do you enjoy making soup?

SpongeBob's Grandma: Oh, yes. It is a stirring experience.

Cracked Up Cookbooks

Sweet Treats by Candy Kane

Picnic Favourites by Frank Furter

The Big Book of Pizza Toppings by Anne Chovey, Tom Maito, and Mead Ball

Double Fudge Cakes and Other High-Calorie Desserts by Rich N. Faddening

The Raw Onion Cookbook by Wendy U. Weepalot

Seven-Course Meals and Other Feasts by Phil Mabelly

Nutty Knock-Knocks

Knock, knock.
Who's there?
Pecan.
Pecan who?
Pecan someone
your own size!

Knock, knock.
Who's there?
Justin.
Justin who?
Justin time for
Krabby Patties.

Knock, knock.
Who's there?
Doughnut
Doughnut who?
Doughnut open till Christmas.

Knock, knock.
Who's there?
Duncan.
Duncan who?
Duncan cookies in
milk is yummy.

Knock, knock.
Who's there?
ice-cream soda.
ice-cream soda who?
ice-scream soda people in
Bikini Bottom can hear me.

Knock, knock.
Who's there?
Lettuce.
Lettuce who?
Lettuce stop telling
these jokes already!

Dear SpongeBob...

A Funny Fill-ins Book

SIMON AND SCHUSTER/NICKELODEON

Hi! It's me, SpongeBob SquarePants! I get a lot of letters asking important questions and I need your help answering them. Are you ready? Here's what you do . . .

Pick a friend to write words in the blanks. He or she will not read the letters out loud until all the blanks have been filled in. The other friend (or friends) will give him or her the words.

When asked for a NOUN, fill in the name of a person, place, or thing. *Clam, seaweed,* and *bucket* are examples of nouns.

When asked for a VERB, fill in an action word. *Eat, wrestle,* and *honk* are examples of verbs. You'll also be asked for an "-ing verb." This means words like *eating, wrestling,* and *honking.* Sometimes you'll be asked for a "past-tense verb." *Ate, wrestled,* and *honked* are examples of past-tense verbs.

An ADJECTIVE is a word that describes a person or a thing, like *pretty, amazing,* or *horrible.*

An ADVERB is a word that describes how something is done, and usually ends with "ly," like *quickly, shyly,* and *seriously.*

You'll also be asked for specific words like "type of food," "type of sea creature," or "number." Just fill in a word that's one of those things.

That's it! I'm ready — let's go!

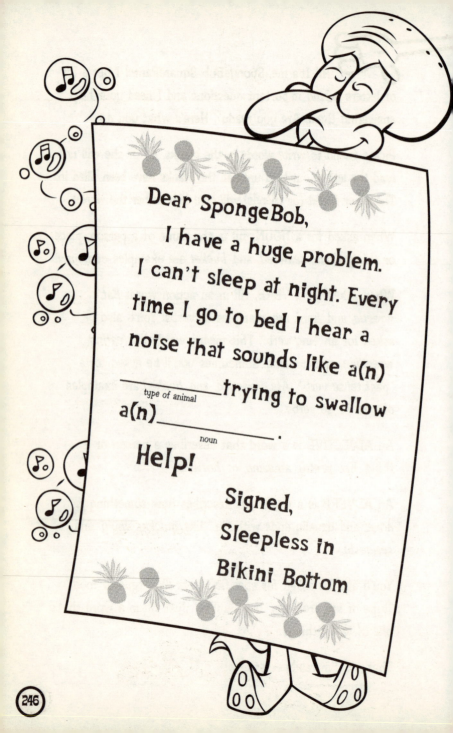

Dear SpongeBob,

I have a huge problem. I can't sleep at night. Every time I go to bed I hear a noise that sounds like a(n) _____ trying to swallow a(n) _____.

type of animal

noun

Help!

Signed,
Sleepless in
Bikini Bottom

Dear Sleepless in Bikini Bottom,

That's just my friend Squidward playing his clarinet! I suggest putting _____
type of lunch meat
in your ears or wearing a(n) _____ over
noun
your head. If this doesn't work, drink
a(n) _____-flavoured glass of warm _____.
noun   *type of liquid*
You can also try counting _____ s
type of sea creature
jumping over _____ s. That always works
noun
for me!

Sweet dreams!

Sleepily yours,
SpongeBob SquarePants

Dear SpongeBob,

I get very nervous when I have to take a test at school. The minute I sit down at my

_____ , my mind goes
          noun

_____ , and I forget
        adjective

everything I _____ .
                    past tense verb

At this rate, I'll be in summer school for the next_____
                                    extremely high number
years!

What can I do?

Signed,

Summer-School Bound

Dear Summer-School Bound,

I know how you feel! Whenever I take a test at Mrs Puff's Boating School my _____ gets
body part
sweaty and my_____ shakes. Sometimes
body part
I can't remember the answers, so I just guess or put down the number_____ . The last time I took
number
my driving test I ran over a(n)_____ ,
noun
crashed into a(n)_____ , and then drove back
noun
to school so slowly that an old_____
type of sea creature
passed me. But someday I will pass the test and become a(n)_____ driver!
adjective

Studiously yours,

SpongeBob
SquarePants

RULES of the ROAD

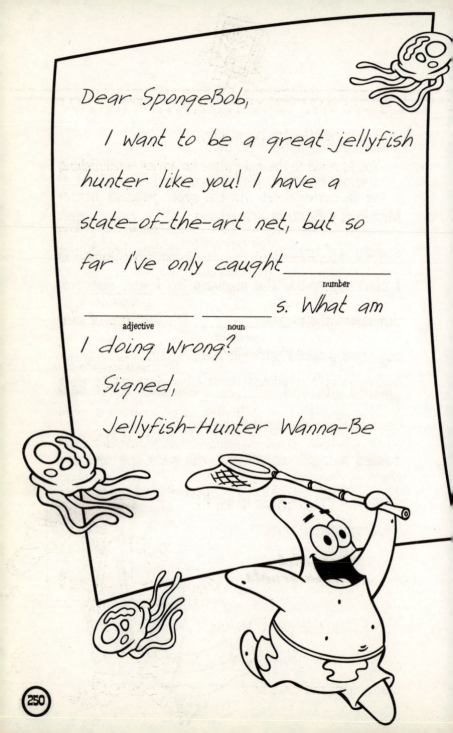

Dear SpongeBob,

I want to be a great jellyfish hunter like you! I have a state-of-the-art net, but so far I've only caught_____
number

_____ _____s. What am
adjective   noun

I doing wrong?

Signed,

Jellyfish-Hunter Wanna-Be

Dear Jellyfish-Hunter Wanna-Be,

You've come to the right place for advice — jellyfishing is my favourite sport! As the great jellyfish hunter

_____ _____ once said: "The
　　a pet's name　　　　　a friend's last name

secret to becoming a(n) _____ jellyfish hunter is
　　　　　　　　　　　　　adjective

having the_____ of a(n)_____ ,
　　　　body part　　　　　　　type of animal

the heart of a(n)_____ , the eyes of a(n)
　　　　　　　type of insect

_____ , and the strength of a(n)_____ ."
type of bird　　　　　　　　　　type of circus performer

I have no idea what that means but it seems to work

for _____ ! It also helps to have a good
　same pet's name

battle cry that sounds like a(n)_____ . Just don't get
　　　　　　　　　　　　　sound

stung. Once I got stung on my _____ _____
　　　　　　　　　　　body part　　　number

times and I couldn't sit down for _____ weeks!
　　　　　　　　　　　　　number

Your pal,

**SpongeBob
SquarePants**

P.S. Don't forget to let the

jellyfish go so you can catch

them again the next day!

251

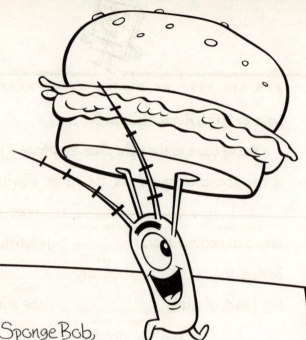

Dear SpongeBob,

I would like to know how to

make the _____ Krabby Patties.
                adjective

I promise not to tell anyone the secret

recipe!

You can trust me,

~~Plankton~~

Joe McSworkelsteen

Dear Mr McSworkelsteen (if that's your real name),

I can never reveal the Krabby Patty recipe! Mr Krabs made me take the sacred Krabby Patty oath of secrecy: "I swear I will never tell the secret of the Krabby Patties! If I do, may my _____ be tickled and my
_____ body part _____
_____ be sprayed with hot_____, and
_____ body part _____   _____ type of liquid _____
may I soak in a bathtub full of _____ juice
_____ type of vegetable _____
and may wild _____s nibble at my toes, and
_____ type of animal _____
may _____ sing_____ in_____
_____ a teacher's name _____   _____ a song title _____   _____ foreign language _____
over and over till I turn_____ and then make me watch
_____ colour _____
_____movies backward!" So you can understand
_____ movie star _____
why I would never tell!

Your krabby pal,

*SpongeBob
SquarePants*

Dear SpongeBob,

I am a(n) _____ fan of
                 adjective

Mermaid Man and Barnacle Boy.

I hear you have a(n) _____
                              adjective

collection of their things. Can

you tell me about it?

Signed,

Mermaid Man Fan

Dear Mermaid Man Fan,

I have a rare Mermaid Man _____ that
article of clothing

smells like a(n) _____ when you put it in
type of sea creature

_____. I also have the Mermaid Man watch
type of liquid

that doesn't tell time because he never learned how. I

have the Barnacle Boy _____ with _____ spring
noun adjective

action that makes it_____ _____ feet per second
verb number

(batteries not included). I also have an autographed

Mermaid Man _____ and a Barnacle Boy
bathroom item

_____that comes in_____ colours and goes
noun number

_____ when you throw it. My favourite thing is a piece
sound

of Mermaid Man_____-flavoured _____ that is
flavor food item

_____ years old and still in perfect condition!
number

Your super friend,
SpongeBob SquarePants

255

Dear SpongeBob,

   I have a friend named SpongeBob
SquarePants! Isn't that _____
                                   adverb
amazing? You both have the same name!

Signed,

Patrick Star

Dear Patrick,

It's me – your best _____ SpongeBob! When I
noun

am not _____ overtime at the Krusty Krab,
-ing verb

I write an advice column for the *Bikini* _____
noun

Times. We just talked about it yesterday, remember?

I told you about the big _____ in my office,
noun

the _____ phone with all the flashing lights,
adjective

and the supply cupboard that is filled with ____s.
noun

Call me – we'll do lunch!

Best,
SpongeBob

Dear SpongeBob,

My friends invited me to a scary movie but I'm too scared to go. I keep making up excuses like, "Sorry, I have to _____ my _____ – maybe next time." But I'm running out of reasons. What should I do?

verb _noun_

Signed,
Scaredy Cat

Dear Scaredy Cat,

Buy a _____-gallon box of popcorn and hide
      high number
behind it when the movie gets_____scary. The
                                adverb
scariest movie I ever saw was *Attack of the*

_____-Foot _____-*Shark Monster.* It was about
number   _type of fruit_
a shark named _____, who was very nice until
              a boy's name
a vampire _____bit him. After that he turned
          type of insect
into a giant_____every time the moon rose.
             noun
His girlfriend,_____, loved him even though he
               a girl's name
ate her_____, her favourite_____,
        musical instrument   _noun_
and all the_____s in the city. My friend Patrick
           noun
hid under his seat the whole time. He missed the

movie, but he found a lot of old _____ on
                                  type of food
the floor to snack on.

Your frightened friend,

SpongeBob
ScaredyPants

Dear Mr Square Pants,

I would like to get a job at the Krusty Krab. I have a lot of experience in fast food. I make excellent _____
_{type of fruit}
and _____ sandwiches, delicious
_{type of vegetable}
fried _____-balls, and the best
_{type of food}
_____ with seaweed sprinkles this
_{type of dessert}
side of the Pacific. Can you help me?

Sincerely yours,

Mr P.

Dear Mr P.,

I am afraid there are no job openings at the Krusty Krab. No one ever quits because it's the most _____ job in the world! When I'm _____ Krabby
_{adjective} ... _{-ing verb}

Patties I feel like the king of the_____! And I don't
_{a place}

just get to make the greatest burgers this side of _____, I get to sweep_____s under the rug,
_{a planet} ... _{noun}

make the bathrooms extra_____ , and watch Mr
_{adjective}

Krabs_____ his money!
_{verb}

Your krusty buddy,

**SpongeBob
SquarePants**

Dear SpongeBob,

My mum only lets me watch _____ hours of
                                    number
television a day. I want to make sure I'm

seeing the_____ ones. What are your
              adjective
favourite TV shows?

Signed,

Couch Potato

262

Dear Couch Potato,

My very favourite TV show is *Mermaid Man and Barnacle Boy*, but I also like *The_____ Man and*
_{noun}

the_____ , _____ for Sand Dollars,
_{type of fish}   _{-ing verb}

The _____ Adventures of Jed _____
_{adjective}   _{type of fish}

_____ , How to _____ Your Snail,
_{type of occupation}   _{verb}

and *Everybody Loves _____ .*
_{type of fish}

Your TV-loving pal,

SpongeBob SquarePants

263

Dear SpongeBob,

There's a bully at school who keeps bothering me. He_____s me when I walk by, _____s my lunch money, and sometimes even stuffs me into a(n)_____! What should I do?

Signed,

Hiding in My Locker

Dear Hiding in My Locker,

Bullies are just nice people trapped inside mean

people's _____s. You could try to win him over by
                 noun

making him a(n) _____ or by inviting him to
                     type of dessert

_____. Or you could do what I do when I see
      a place

a bully: _____ away as fast as a(n) _____,
            verb   type of animal

screaming like a(n) _____ !
                         type of bird

Safe at home,

SpongeBob SquarePants

Dear SpongeBob,

What kind of music do you like?
I'm tired of all my_____s and would
like some new_____s to listen to.
Are there any_____s from Bikini
Bottom that I should check out?
Signed,
Singing Fool

Dear Singing Fool,

I love music! One of my favourite bands is The

_____ _____ Experience. My
type of sea creature   type of fruit

favourite songs by them are "_____ in the
                                a girl's name

_____ with_____s," and "If You Were My _____I'd
noun   noun   noun

_____ with You All Day Long Except _____."
verb   day of the week

My friend Patrick's favourite band is The_____-Note
                                         low number

Band. They only play _____ note(s) and they only
                      same number

know one song called "This Song Is Hard to Play." My

friend Sandy loves The Texas _____ Boots (featuring
                             adjective

Betty Sue_____ on _____). Squidward
         type of sandwich   musical instrument

likes The _____ -Clarinet Orchestra and Louis
          high number

_____and the_____ Hot Clams.
type of fish   number

Musically yours,

SpongeBob SquarePants

Dear SpongeBob,

   I am throwing a party next week and I want it to be great. We're going to play pin the _____ on the _____, musical

       noun   type of animal

_____s, and capture the _____. But

  noun   noun

I need help figuring out what else to do.

Any advice?

Signed,

Party Hearty

Dear Party Hearty,

   The secret to a good party is good food, good music, and good friends! My favourite party foods are pizza with _____ and _____ on top,
<u>type of breakfast food</u>   <u>type of candy</u>

_____ cupcakes, and of course, Krabby
<u>type of lunch meat</u>

Patties. I know all the latest dance moves, so if you invite me to your fun party I'll show everyone how to do "The Funky_____," "The _____ _____,"
<u>noun</u>   <u>adjective</u>   <u>noun</u>

and "The _____ Twist." Most importantly, you
<u>type of hat</u>

need good friends at a party! They can help you clean up. And like my friend Patrick always says, "A party without friends is a like a _____ without a(n)
<u>noun</u>

_____ in the_____."
<u>car part</u>   <u>season</u>

Good luck,

SpongeBob
SquarePants

Dear SpongeBob,

I'm thinking about getting a pet snail.

Snails are so _____ and _____ .
                 adjective   adjective

Can you tell me about your pet snail, Gary?

Signed,

I Like Gary

Dear I Like Gary,

Gary is _____ special! He's a purebred snail
            adverb

directly descended from _____, the _____
                          a boy's name   adjective

snail from the fourteenth century who saved the

_____ Wall of _____ from burning down
adjective   name of city

by sliming it. Gary can do _____ tricks! He can
                              high number

jump over a(n) _____, he knows how to say "meow"
                 noun

in _____ languages, and he does a perfect imitation
    number

of _____ . Gary and I really like to play
    movie star

hide-and- _____. I always hide in my _____
            verb   type of room

and he always finds me by using his _____ .
                                        body part

Gary is the greatest pet a sponge could have!

Your partner in slime,

*SpongeBob
SquarePants*

271

Dear SpongeBob,

Guess what? I am in the Mermaid Man and Barnacle Boy Fan Club too! We should meet up at the _____
a place
for a(n) _____ and _____
type of food   type of drink
and swap trading cards. What is your favourite Mermaid Man and Barnacle Boy adventure?

Signed,
MM & BB Forever

Dear MM & BB Forever,

I love *all* the Mermaid Man and Barnacle Boy Adventures, but my favourite is "Mermaid Man Meets the _____ s of the
                                                        type of occupation
_____ Empire of Space Dinosaurs." It's the one where Mermaid
    adjective
Man is captured by Man Ray, put in a(n) _____, and sent into
                                              type of pastry
space in a(n)_____ . Meanwhile Barnacle Boy can't find Mermaid
                 noun
Man so he hangs up his_____ and gets a job at a(n)
                              article of clothing
_____ _____ _____ s. Mermaid Man is
   place of work   -ing verb   noun
turned into a(n)_____ and held prisoner inside a _____
                     noun   type of room
and forced to make _____s. He escapes using a(n)_____,
                       type of toy   kitchen item
and a space dinosaur named _____ helps him build a space
                                a girl's name
ship out of _____to return home! Mermaid Man finds Barnacle
               type of fruit
Boy, who is now selling_____s door-to-door. The two heroes
                            noun
are reunited; they capture Man Ray and find out that he is Mermaid

Man's _____'s _____'s _____'s
          type of relative   type of relative   type of relative
_____'s best friend!
   type of relative

Up, up, and away!

SpongeBob
SquarePants

Dear SpongeBob,

I keep having the same _____
adjective
nightmare about _____
a teacher's name
shrinking down to the size of a(n)

_____ and moving into my
type of insect

_____ drawer. Do you
article of clothing
ever have weird dreams?

Signed,

Dream Weaver

Dear Dream Weaver,

    I had a(n) _____ _____ dream last night! I
                 adverb   adjective

lived in an oversized _____ and rode to work on
                     type of hat

a(n) _____ . But I wasn't working at the
      type of animal

Krusty Krab — I had a job at the Chum Bucket! I had to

make plankton patties and sing songs about _____s!
                               noun

The plankton patties were made out of _____ flakes,
                         noun

_____ goo, and_____ chunks. I ate one and it tasted
noun   noun

like a(n)_____. And then my friends walked in and
      noun

they all looked_____ weird! Patrick was a(n)_____,
           adverb   noun

Sandy was a(n) _____ , Squidward was a(n)
            type of occupation

_____ , and Gary was a man-eating_____.
type of plant   type of bird

Boy was I glad to wake up!

Sleeping with one eye open,

**SpongeBob
SquarePants**

Dear SpongeBob,

Why are you of all people giving advice! I
should be doing it! The readers need someone
who is _____ smart and _____ intellectual!
          adverb   adverb
I know about _____ in _____, where
                    -ing verb   a country
_____ go to _____, and the difference
type of fish   verb
between _____ s and _____
          type of vegetables   type of dance
. . . unlike some people I know.

Signed,

Squidward

Dear Squidward,

I would love your help writing these letters! It would be the greatest thing since _____
a famous person
went _____ in _____ and discovered the
-ing verb   a place
first_____ . There's plenty of room at my _____
noun   type of furniture
for both of us. We could sit side by side and go out for

_____ and eat with our _____ s and take
type of food   body part
long walks in the_____ together. We'll be joined at
noun
the _____ — it'll be great!
body part

Your *pen* pal,

SpongeBob

Dear SpongeBob,

I want to get a surprise gift for my best friend. Last year I got him a(n) _____-flavoured _____
type of fruit   article of clothing
and a pet_____. What do you
noun
think he would like? He is yellow and square and spongy.

Thank you,

Patrick Star

P.S. Don't tell SpongeBob I'm getting him a gift! It's a secret!

Dear Patrick,

Thanks, pal, but you don't have to get me a gift!

Although I did like the_____ made out
                                                              type of board game

of_____you gave me on _____!
     type of candy   day of the week

Your friend,

SpongeBob

Dear SpongeBob,

Is the Flying Dutchman real or imaginary? I made a bet with my friend that he's real. If I win the bet, she has to _____ my _____s until
  verb   noun
_____; if she wins, I have to _____
month   verb
her_____s until _____! Can you
    noun   month
settle our bet?

Signed,

Fingers Crossed

Dear Fingers Crossed,

The Flying Dutchman is as real as a(n)＿＿＿＿＿!
noun

And so are Santa Claus, the Easter＿＿＿＿＿＿,
type of animal

the Tooth ＿＿＿＿＿＿＿＿, and the＿＿＿＿＿
type of occupation   adjective

＿＿＿＿＿that goes＿＿＿＿ in the＿＿＿＿＿
type of fish   sound   time of day

and brings＿＿＿＿＿to good little boys and girls!
type of candy

Your best bet,

*SpongeBob
SquarePants*

Dear SpongeBob,

You have a(n) _____ sense of
                    adjective
style – I just love the _____
                              adjective
fashions you wear. How can I become

a(n) _____ dresser like you?
           adjective
Signed,

Clothes Horse

Dear Clothes Horse,

Everyone should have a white shirt, tie, short pants, athletic socks, and shoes in their wardrobe! But when you play _____ you should wear a(n)
type of sport

_____, tight _____ pants, and size_____
type of hat   colour   size

sneakers. If you go out on the town to_____
verb

someplace fancy, you should wear a(n) _____
type of flower

in your lapel and carry a(n)_____. And make
noun

sure your shoes are _____ and your socks are
adjective

_____ .
adjective

All dressed up and

nowhere to_____ ,
verb

SpongeBob
SquarePants

Howdy, SpongeBob!

How the _____s are you? I'm in Texas right now — the
          noun

_____ place in the world! You would love it here,
   adjective

SpongeBob. They're having a(n) _____ Karate
                                        adjective

Jamboree, a(n) _____ rodeo, and a(n)
                        type of insect

_____festival all in the same week! I'll bring
   type of dance

you a(n) _____-gallon cowboy hat, a giant box
            high number

of hot chili _____s, and some chocolate-covered
                  food item

_____s shaped like a Texas _____. Wish
   noun   type of reptile

you were here!

Yee Haw,

Sandy

P.S. Don't forget to water my _____s and feed my
                                        noun

_____s.
   noun

Dear Sandy,

That sounds _____! I can't wait to hear all
                adjective

about your _____ trip! Take lots of _____s
            adjective   noun

and hurry back, y'all!

Your karate-chopping buddy,

SpongeBob

Dear SpongeBob,

I got the lead _____ in my school
                   noun

play "The Importance of Being

_____ ." I am very nervous!
type of sandwich

Help!

Signed,

Sweaty Palms

Dear Sweaty Palms,

Just relax and don't do what I did! I was in a play at the

Bikini Bottom _____ Theatre called "King Neptune
type of meal

and the _____ _____ ." I had to wear a(n)
adjective noun

_____ made out of_____ fur. My
article of clothing type of animal

sword got tangled in the fur and I tripped and fell on my

_____ . I started sweating like a(n)_____ .
body part type of sea creature

I only had one line: "I have a message for the king in my

pocket that must be sent to France by pigeon." Instead I

said, "I have a(n)_____ for the_____ in my
noun type of occupation

_____ that must to be sent to_____ by
article of clothing a planet

a(n)_____ ." Patrick thought it was the_____
type of fish -est adjective

line he'd ever heard.

Your fellow nervous actor,

SpongeBob
SquarePants

Thanks for all of your help

with these letters. So long!

Ever your pen pal,

*SpongeBob
SquarePants*